KARLEEN BRADFORD

ANIMAL HEROES

Cover by
SHARIF TARABAY

SCHOLASTIC INC.
New York Toronto London Auckland Sydney

ISBN 0-590-18796-1

Copyright © 1995 by Karleen Bradford.
All rights reserved. Published by Scholastic Inc., 555 Broadway, New York, NY 10012, by arrangement with Scholastic Canada, Ltd.

SCHOLASTIC and associated logos are trademarks and/or registered trademarks of Scholastic Inc.

12 11 10 9 8   4 5 6 7 8 9/0

Printed in the U.S.A.   40

First Scholastic printing, May 1998

Contents

For Cindy, Phoebe, Prince and Tiff: my own family's special friends.

Acknowledgments

I would like to thank the owners of these brave animals for telling me their stories. They were patient with me and with my interminable questions, and very generous with their time. I enjoyed getting to know them and their wonderful companions, even though my own dog and cat got a little suspicious of all the alien-smelling animal hair that kept coming home on my clothes!

As well, I would like to thank Sid Horton, George Hickinbottom, and Jim Allaway, editor of the *Navy News* in Portsmouth, England, for the information and anecdotes they sent to me about Simon, the Ship's Cat.

Bill and Jane Thornton, of Canadian Guide Dogs for the Blind, in Manotick, Ontario, were also extremely helpful.

I have Tony German, of Old Chelsea, Quebec, to thank for the story of the rabbit, and for background information from his book, *The Sea Is At Our Gates: The History of the Canadian Navy* (McClelland & Stewart, 1990).

I would also like to thank Ralston Purina Canada, Inc., for their assistance, and particularly Sylvia Sharp of National Public Relations (NPR) Limited. In 1968, Ralston Purina established an Animal Hall of Fame to honour the heroic deeds of Canadian pets. Every year, they induct several animals into the Hall of Fame, flying them and their owners from all over Canada into Toronto for the award ceremony. Hall of Fame inductees included in this book are:

Cali	Grizzly	Nago
Charlie	Hustler	Shana
Euchre	Nellie	*and* Tia.

Karleen Bradford

CALI

The Guard Cat

There was a cage full of kittens at the Toronto Humane Society animal shelter when Lauren MacLaren went to pick out a pet. They had been found abused and tossed away in a bag. Four of them were males: black, white or orange. They were tumbling around and wrestling with each other. As soon as they spotted Lauren, they clambered over each other excitedly in their efforts to get her attention. But Lauren was looking at their tiny, frightened, calico-patterned sister, huddled away in a corner at the back. Lauren knew this was the kitten she'd come to find.

She brought Cali home with her, and during the next six years they became the best of friends. "She's my shadow," Lauren says. "Everywhere I go, she goes."

One night Lauren was sleeping in her ground floor bedroom. It was almost two o'clock in the morning. Suddenly Cali leaped up onto the bed and pounced on Lauren. Lauren woke with a start. Confused and half asleep, she couldn't imagine what was the matter with her cat. Cali pawed at her, crying, then started a low, rumbling kind of growl. She wouldn't leave Lauren alone.

Finally, Lauren sat up, thoroughly awake. At that moment she heard a crunching noise outside the bedroom door, which opened onto the deck outside. It was footsteps, coming stealthily up the driveway! She heard them come up onto the deck. She heard them come closer. Then, to her horror, she saw the doorknob begin to turn.

The door was locked, but as the knob rattled, Lauren panicked. The house she lived in was old. Just how strong was the wooden door?

There was a telephone beside the bed, but the window beside the door was open a crack. Lauren was afraid that if she used the bedroom phone the intruder outside her door would hear. Carefully, she slipped out of bed and crawled into the kitchen. As soon as Cali realized that her friend was aware of the danger and was doing something about it, she did the only thing a sensible cat would do. She hid under the bed.

As quietly as she could, Lauren phoned 9-1-1.

"The people on 9-1-1 were wonderful," Lauren says now. "They calmed me right down. I was terrified. Your imagination does go a little crazy in a situation like that. But they kept me on the phone and they told me not to worry — I might not see the police, but they had been called and were already there."

And they were. Within minutes the intruder was captured, right on Lauren's back deck, and placed under arrest. And Cali watched it all — from under the bed's dust ruffle.

Cali received the Ralston Purina Animal Hall of Fame Award for her quick intelligence and for the alertness that saved Lauren from an intruder that night. Cali took her place proudly at the ceremony, right by Hustler, the German Shepherd, and Tia, the chocolate Lab, who were also being honoured that year.

"She looked so small up there, beside those two big dogs," Lauren says. "And they'd done such brave things to save their masters — fight off coyotes and pull a boat to shore . . . " Lauren laughs, but her voice is full of pride. "Maybe cats can't do the things dogs can do, but they are very aware. The instinct is there. She knew those footsteps weren't normal for that time of night, and she knew she had to wake me up. Mind you," she adds, "once she knew I was awake, that was it. I mean, she wasn't going to stand around and bare her teeth at anybody!"

Besides the medal and several other prizes, Cali won a year's supply of cat food. To express her thanks for her friend, Lauren donated it all to the animal shelter that brought them together.

Cali

Racing Sled Dogs

The best racing sled dogs are Alaskan Huskies, a mix of purebred Siberian Huskies and Border Collies or hounds such as Salukis or Greyhounds. The Husky part gives these dogs their toughness and ability to withstand the cold, the hound or Border Collie part gives them their speed.

Although this is not a registered breed, each dog has a pedigree of its own. Every one of the eleven dogs in a team is scrupulously cared for. When racing on icy snow and rough tracks, they wear specially fitted boots.

Racing dogs are not pets. They live in a kennel. They snarl and growl and fight among themselves. But with people they are loving, gentle dogs. When Paul Guitard's young children are in the kennel with him they're in and out of the doghouses, playing with them all the time.

"These sled dogs," Paul says, "the only way they're going to hurt you is if they lick you to death."

GRIZZLY

The Dog Who Fought a Bear

It was about ten o'clock on a warm June morning when Paul Guitard decided to take his sled dogs for a run. As usual in the summer months, he harnessed his team up to his four-wheel all-terrain vehicle. His lead dog was a black and silver-grey purebred Siberian Husky named Grizzly.

A few years before, Paul had bought a Siberian Husky named Kiska, just because he liked the looks of the breed. After he got her he went to a sled dog race and thought it looked like fun. He became more and more interested, and finally decided to buy a male, build up his own team, and see what he could do.

Grizzly was the male Paul chose, and soon Kiska had puppies. "I kept a bunch and started hooking them up to a sled, and first thing you know, *I got hooked!*" Paul says.

Over the years, Grizzly helped Paul train the young dogs, and eventually one of them took over as lead dog of Paul's racing team. But even the fastest dog can't replace Grizzly in the hearts of Paul and his family. For loyal, steadfast Grizzly is more than a sled dog — he's a hero.

On that warm June morning, with Grizzly in the lead, the dogs were running well. They were about three kilometres down the trail when suddenly, out of nowhere, a black bear charged out of the bush. Before Paul had time to realize what was happening, the bear was on top of him and savagely biting his leg and arm.

"I looked over and saw two cubs on the path — we'd come between them and their mother — and I thought, *Uh, oh. I'm in trouble!* Then, all of a sudden, the bear pulled me right off my bike. The dogs went on a hundred metres or so and I thought they were gone."

Normally, if Paul falls off or loses the team, the

dogs just keep right on going. But Grizzly knew Paul was in trouble. He brought the team to a halt, turned them all — and the bike — and headed back to Paul. In harness and *still attached to the rest of the team*, Grizzly went for the bear. The bear released Paul and turned to fight the dog; Paul scrambled for the nearest tree. As he started up it, the bear's jaws closed on his right foot.

"I was kicking her with my other foot, trying to make her let me go, and she was pulling me back down the tree," Paul recalls. "Then Grizzly went at her again and started biting at her, so she let me go. I climbed up to the top of the tree — fast!"

Grizzly stationed himself at the bottom of the tree, between Paul and the bear. The cubs ran to the other side of the trail and up a tree of their own.

"I expected that when everything calmed down everybody would leave," Paul says. The cubs left after about two hours, but their mother stayed. Every twenty minutes or so she made another rush for the tree, and each time Grizzly fought her off. When he charged, the harness pulled all the other dogs forward too, but *they* weren't about to help fight a bear. In fact, just to add to Grizzly's problems, they began to fight among themselves —

until Grizzly sorted them out.

The day became hotter. Paul sat in the tree, sweating, knowing he was going to be there for a while, until someone missed him and started trying to find him. His right arm and leg were bleeding badly, and he was in a lot of pain.

"I just sat up there and waited," he says, "and every time the bear charged the tree I wondered, is she going to get up this time?"

But Grizzly kept her away. After three or four hours, the bear ambled about 200 metres off and settled herself down to sleep. Paul began to think about sneaking down the tree, unhooking the dogs, and getting away on the bike. Cautiously, he began to climb down.

"I got about halfway down. She put her head up, looked at me, and gave a kind of a grunt. She started to get up. 'Hey, no problem!' I said, and headed back up my tree."

About an hour after that — six hours since the bear attacked — Paul finally heard more all-terrain vehicles coming. He knew it was probably his brother-in-law and friend coming to look for him. Paul screamed at them to go home and get a gun, so they turned around.

"That was the toughest time," Paul says now, "because I was so close to getting saved, and if she got up there before they got back . . . " He broke a branch off the tree and made a little spear out of it — anything to keep the bear away if she did get up. But Grizzly remained on guard, and the bear didn't get through.

At last Paul heard his friends returning. The bear heard them too. She crossed over to the other side of the trail and waited for them. Just as they came into sight, she charged. She was only a few metres away when Paul's friend shot her. Paul stayed where he was long enough to make sure the bear was really dead; then, fighting pain and fatigue, he clambered down the tree.

The first thing he did was tend to Grizzly. The dog had only a small gash on his nose where one of the bear's claws had caught him. In spite of being hampered by the harness and all the other dogs, he had still managed to be faster on his feet than the lumbering bear.

Paul, however, had a gash on his right arm and the calf of his right leg was cut open. And he found out later that he had broken his left ankle from kicking the bear in the nose.

"Not that it did much good," he says now. "I think it only made her madder. It was Grizzly who saved me. I can honestly say, and I've said it a hundred times, I wouldn't be here if it weren't for that dog. I'd be dead. That bear would have killed me."

When he got home and had had his wounds tended to, Paul worried about the cubs whose mother had been shot. An animal biologist who called to talk to him about it later on assured him that the cubs were probably old enough to take care of themselves by then. He also said that the bear's behaviour in not going after her cubs once they had left was so unusual that there must have been something wrong.

Grizzly is older now, and has slowed down a little. But he still races with Paul's son. He has a privileged place among all the other dogs. When Paul is away, his wife Jan brings Grizzly into the house for company. The dog who faced down a bear loves being a family pet; he'll happily let the children pull his ears and maul him to their hearts' content.

"He's just a happy-go-lucky, never-does-anything-wrong dog," Paul says, his voice full of affection and pride.

Grizzly (front left), Paul and team

Hustler

HUSTLER

The Dog Who Wouldn't Quit

Debbie Inions went to a dog show and fell in love with a six-month-old black and tan German Shepherd. She asked his owners if he was for sale, but they said no. Two months later they called Debbie to offer her the dog. Although they loved him and thought the world of him, he wasn't working out for them. He was a "very relaxed kind of dog," and just didn't do well in the competitive atmosphere of the show ring. Since he'd been brought up in a house with children and was "a real spoiled couch potato," Debbie was sure that he would make a good pet for her children. She brought the pup home to their farm, and named him Hustler.

The Inions have a herd of cattle, and Debbie decided to see if she could also make a working dog out of Hustler. He had never even seen a cow before, but he seemed to know what to do. Calving was starting, and they were getting the heifers into the barn. Hustler jumped right in, nipping at their heels and moving them along. Within a short while he was working with Debbie and her husband, Brian, getting cattle into the chute, loading them, cutting out cows that needed help — anything that had to be done, he could do it. "It was like having two extra guys around to help," Debbie says.

She also says he's "quite the character." When he's working cattle, Hustler can be as aggressive as he needs to be to get the job done. At other times, Hustler strolls right through the herd without causing any problems at all. Sometimes he even sleeps with the cows. Debbie says, "He's got two different sides to him. He knows when he's on duty and when he's off. He's a real sweetheart."

It's true. His previous owner kept birds — cockatiels and little budgies — and let them fly loose in her house. Hustler once found one downstairs and carried it gently upstairs between his teeth to lay it at her feet, completely unharmed. He even helped her retrieve some baby birds that had fallen out of a nest — he found one on the ground and carried it back to her.

Hustler did have to learn about horses, though. One of them in particular didn't appreciate dogs running too close to his heels. It took a few minor kicks, and then one bad one that required surgery to an eye, for Hustler to get the message. Hustler still happily runs with horses — at a respectful distance.

One evening, after she had settled Tracy and Curtis down for the night, Debbie decided to make a last check on the cattle. Brian was out seeding barley in one of the fields, and she knew he would be working late to get it all done that night. She figured she would be gone for half an hour at most. She mounted her quarter horse and, together with Hustler, headed into the bush toward the field where the cattle were.

As they were going up a hill, a sudden noise at the top caused Debbie's horse to shy. He jumped sideways, down the hill. Debbie, a good horse-woman, managed to stay on; but then, because there was a fence in front of the spooked horse and he couldn't run straight out, he spun around. There was a brush pile there, and he jumped again. This time Debbie was thrown.

"I landed on my leg," Debbie says. "Before the rest of me even hit the ground, I knew it was broken." (In fact, two bones had been broken in three places.)

Debbie lay dazed, the pain from her leg almost overwhelming her. The horse, calm now, ambled over and sniffed at her, perhaps curious about why she wasn't getting back on. Debbie realized that she was not going to be able to move. She'd taken a shortcut through the bush and knew there was no chance of anyone happening upon her there. She thought if she could send her horse home and someone saw him they might come looking for her.

"I threw sticks at him and stuff, and kind of chased him away. He went, but he went back the way we had come, which was through bushes and behind the barn where he couldn't be seen by anybody. I knew that wasn't going to be much help."

All the while, Hustler stayed by her side. Then suddenly he went charging off through the bush.

Debbie thought, *Well, that's just fine. Here I am with a broken leg and he's off chasing some deer.*

"I never thought anything more about it, but then he was back, standing over me, and he was snarling. All I could see were his teeth, and he looked so vicious! I'd never seen him look like that, because he's not a vicious dog. I looked over my shoulder, in the the direction he was looking, and there were two coyotes snarling back at him."

The coyotes were only about four metres away, and inching closer. Hustler jumped over Debbie and attacked. They ran off into the bushes, and he followed. Debbie watched them disappear.

"I didn't know who was going to come back, Hustler or the coyotes," she says.

Finally Hustler did return, but so did the coyotes. Evening darkened into night. Every time Hustler chased the coyotes away, they came stubbornly back. Debbie's leg was bleeding heavily; the scent of the blood must have been irresistible to them.

"It got quite scary," Debbie says now. "Each time I just wondered how much longer he was going to be able to keep those coyotes off me, and when was it going to be the coyotes that came back through the bush instead of him?"

But Hustler came back every time. Debbie got weaker, and started shaking with shock and cold. She wrapped her arms around Hustler and pressed herself as close as she could to the warmth of his body. The coyotes didn't give up. They came back again and again. Again and again, Hustler tore himself away to go after them. The black night was filled with their howling.

Brian Inions got home about one-thirty in the morning. He was tired, but the barley crop was all planted. The house was quiet; he figured Debbie and the children were asleep. He started to get himself something to eat. Then he realized that Debbie's boots were gone. He looked out and saw that her horse was gone, too. He went in to Tracy, woke her, and asked if she knew where Debbie was. Tracy murmured that her mother had gone out to check the cows. Only half awake, she didn't realize what the time was.

Brian jumped on their all-terrain vehicle and roared out to look for Debbie. There was a lot of land to cover, however. A lot of hills and bush. After two hours of fruitless searching, he still hadn't found her. Then he saw Hustler break into a clearing in hot pursuit of two coyotes, and he knew Debbie couldn't be far away.

"I hardly had any voice by that time, I was so weak," Debbie says. "I'd been yelling at the coyotes, and Hustler had been barking at them. In between chasing them he'd come and sit over me just like he was guarding me."

By following Hustler, Brian finally found Debbie. He realized that she was in too much pain for him to try to move her or take her back on the all-terrain vehicle. He would have to go back alone and telephone for an ambulance.

"I suddenly panicked when he left, thinking that Hustler might go back after him," Debbie says. "Then I'd be left alone with those coyotes. It was pitch dark and starting to spit rain. The wind had come up, and I was really cold. Then I looked up and there was Hustler, sitting right by me, just like he had been all the night."

Brian was back as soon as possible with blankets. He wrapped Debbie up in them, and together they waited. The ambulance managed to make it down the trail, arriving soon after. But even while they were loading Debbie into it, even with all the people there, the coyotes still circled, relentless and stubborn.

Debbie was in the hospital for two weeks. During all that time, Hustler worried. Every time Brian came home, the dog would run out hopefully to greet the truck, only to be disappointed when Debbie wasn't in it. When Debbie finally did come home, the first thing he did was sniff her injured leg from hip to ankle, almost as if to make certain she was all right.

Today, Hustler is still a working dog on the Inions' farm. And he's still never far from Debbie's side.

The Akita

Akitas were bred for hunting bear, deer and wild boar in the rugged mountains of northern Japan. At one time only the royal family and other rulers of Japan were allowed to own Akitas. Now this breed has become so widely known and beloved in its home country that the Japanese government designated the dog a national monument and treasure. To the Japanese, the Akita is a symbol of good health. Small Akita statues are given as get-well gifts to sick people, or to newborn babies as a wish for long life, health and happiness.

The Akita is a big, heavy-set, muscular dog, with upstanding ears, a sturdy body with a short, thick coat, and a tail that curls luxuriously over its back. It can be white or tawny brown, with dark streaks or patches. Tawny and spotted dogs have dark masks or blazes on their faces.

Akitas are affectionate and loyal with family and friends, and fierce in defending them against strangers. In times past, Japanese mothers would even leave their children to the care of these dogs.

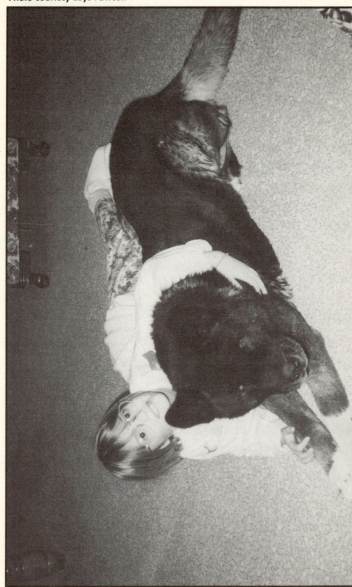

Nago and Alaina

NAGO

The Dog Babysitter

Jeff and Loys Fawcett got their Akita, Nago, when he was seven weeks old. As a puppy he was the centre of attention in their household — almost like a first child. So when the Fawcetts had their first baby, they were a little worried. But Nago wasn't jealous at all. He licked the baby on the back of the head until she was soaking wet, and from that moment on, Lynn and then her sisters Alaina and Elizabeth were Nago's special charges.

"If anyone comes into the yard when the girls are playing outside, Nago just puts himself between the person and the children and won't let them near him," Loys says. "He doesn't growl — just stands there and looks mean."

Nago is a fierce guard dog when he thinks it's necessary, and not only with the children. When the family is out, he's often tied outside. A man working on the house one day came up and offered him half a sandwich. Nago took it, then dropped it on the ground. He wouldn't eat it. The man persisted, and put his hand out to touch Nago. Luckily he was wearing thick gloves. Nago discouraged him with a bite that wasn't quite hard enough to break through the glove, but hard enough to let the man know he was on duty and didn't like strangers around, even if they brought sandwiches. Two hours later when Loys came home, the sandwich was still lying untouched on the ground, and the workman was keeping his distance.

And one night, a man approached Loys when she was walking Nago. She still isn't sure what the man's intentions were, but he never had a chance to make them clear. Before he could get near her, Nago snarled, snapped, and lunged for him. The dog was on the lead and it took all of her strength for Loys to hold him back.

But for all his fierceness, Nago is a quiet dog, and well aware of his own size. Normally, he's careful not to bump or push too hard against anyone, especially the children. He is so friendly and gentle that he is a favourite visitor at schools where Loys takes him to teach children dog manners — what they should or shouldn't do around dogs. He visits hospitals, where patients love to pat him. He snuffles up to touch noses, making friends immediately. At one hospital there was an elderly man who wouldn't respond to anyone, just sat for hours in his wheelchair, staring at nothing, his hands clasped in his lap. When Loys brought Nago into that ward, the first person Nago went up to was that man. He stuck his nose into the man's stomach and laid his head on his lap. The old man's face lit up and he started fondling the dog's ears. It turned out he was a farmer who had had a big dog of his own before he'd become ill, and Nago must have triggered memories of his own pet.

Gentle or not, Nago has a *lot* of energy. To run some of it off, Loys and Jeff will often take him out and let him run behind the car on the country roads near where they live. Thirty kilometres an hour is just fine for him, even at ten years old. Because of this more-than-usual need for exercise, Loys lets him run loose whenever possible.

Nago was loose one cold March morning when Loys, Lynn, Alaina and Elizabeth set out for the stop sign at the top of the hill to wait for the school bus. It looked like it was going to be a warm day, just like the day before, though there had been a freeze overnight and it was still icy underfoot. Nago bounded along in the fields beside the girls. When they got to the road, Loys called Nago to heel and commanded him to sit beside her. Six-year-old Alaina started to play in the dirt beside the stop sign, the other two girls were with Loys.

"Nago doesn't break a command," Loys says, "but he will put variations on it. He'll obey, but it's got to be on his terms." Today Nago sat obediently when she told him to, but faced the opposite way from Loys, who was watching for the bus.

So, Nago was the only one who saw the truck coming up the hill toward them, towing a manure spreader. Only Nago saw the truck hit an icy patch and skid out of control. Only Nago saw the huge manure spreader jackknife, and head straight for Alaina.

Nago hurled himself at Alaina, nearly knocking

her off her feet. She grabbed for a handful of his fur in order to keep from being bowled over, and found herself being dragged away from the road. "You dumb dog!" she cried.

All this happened in just seconds. "Nago and Alaina suddenly appeared in front of me and I realized he'd broken my command," Loys says. She was going to scold Nago when Lynn shouted: "Alaina was just about hit!"

Loys whirled around. The manure spreader was inches away from the stop sign where Alaina had been playing moments before. The truck driver was sitting in shock, his head down on his hands on the steering wheel. Loys and Lynn dove for Nago.

"Good dog!" they cried.

"What's so good about him stepping on me?" Alaina complained.

Today, Loys shakes her head. "I don't know whether animals actually think things out or not," she says, "but I do know that Nago never breaks a command, and when he saw that truck coming for Alaina, he saved her."

Nellie and Ken

NELLIE

The Dog Who Knew What To Do

Nellie is a big black and tan German Shepherd with gentle eyes. She's had a litter of nine purebred pups, and one unexpected romance with a dog that jumped through the window. She used to belong to Ken Emerson's grandson, but when he got married and moved into town, Ken took Nellie home. He's a tobacco farmer, and there's lots of room for Nellie to run where he lives. Nellie had known Ken and his wife Pauline for a long time, even stayed with them when their grandson visited, so she didn't mind the change. She loves to go with Ken on his trips around the farm. Lucky for him — because

31

this probably saved his life.

One afternoon Ken came home about two-thirty, after a meeting in the community. He wanted to check the irrigation dam on his property because there were plans for another dam up above it. The going was rough, so he decided to take the tractor. He scribbled a quick note to Pauline telling her what time it was, where he was going, and that he'd be back shortly. As he started up the tractor, Nellie trotted up, tail wagging expectantly. He almost told her to stay, then changed his mind. It would be a good run for her.

After checking the dam, Ken went around to the back end of the farm to see if there was any switchgrass coming up in the summer fallow. There was a log across the road to discourage trespassers, so he pulled off the road and took a detour around it. This meant going up a fairly steep incline. As he started up the hill, he felt the front end of the tractor lift.

"I let the tractor roll back and tried to hold it with the brakes," Ken said. "I thought the best thing to do would be to turn around and go down the hill head first, rather than try to back down."

But the front end caught, the tractor tipped and

before he realized what was happening, Ken was thrown off. The tractor rolled right over him, then rolled over a couple more times until it reached the bottom of the hill.

The next thing he knew, Ken was lying on the ground, alone in the sudden silence except for his dog. Strangely enough, he felt no pain. Nellie was sitting, looking at him, about ten metres away.

"I went to slide myself down the hill to her," Ken said, "but when I tried to move, my legs spread-eagled and I couldn't put them back together. I thought that maybe my right leg was broken, but I could hear the bones in my pelvis kind of grit together."

In shock, he still didn't feel any pain. *Well, I'll crawl back to the road*, thought Ken, hoping somebody would come along in an hour or so. But he soon realized he wasn't going to make it. Then he thought about Nellie.

"I thought, somehow or other I've got to get word to Pauline, because I was back in where nobody would see me. The only thing I could think of was to send something back with Nellie that they might recognize."

Ken always carries a jackknife, so he reached into

his pocket and took it out, then started to cut up his shirt. It was a heavy shirt, and not easy to rip, but he finally managed to slit it up the seam to the pocket and cut a piece off.

"Nellie, come," he called.

The dog came up to him. He gave her a pat, and tied the shirt onto her collar. Then came the problem of how to make her understand what he needed her to do. Ken's grandson had obedience-trained Nellie. She would stay if told to, even "be nice" if other dogs were around, but Ken didn't know if she'd ever been taught the command to go home. He had to try, though. "Go home," he ordered.

Nellie moved about a metre away, looking worried, then sat down again.

"Go home!" Ken repeated.

She moved another metre away.

"Nellie, go home. Go home, Nellie!" he said as sternly as he could.

She got up, and with a last worried look at him, disappeared into the bushes.

"I figured, well, I guess I've done everything I can do," Ken says now.

After the dog left, Ken must have drifted in and out of consciousness. "Things went kind of grey," he says. He remembers staring at the cloudy, overcast sky. He remembers the ground being cold — so cold! — even though it was May. And he remembers ants.

"I would never have thought there'd be so many ants around," he says. They crawled all over him.

Pauline arrived home from shopping with her sister around four o'clock. She found Ken's note with the time at the top of it and was surprised that he wasn't back yet. She looked out the window and saw Nellie sitting up by the neighbours' house with what looked like a rag or something tied around her neck. She called the dog and untied the shirt, then called the neighbours to see if they had put it on her for some reason. When they assured her they hadn't, she looked more closely at the piece of cloth and recognized it as being cut from the shirt Ken had been wearing that day. She knew then that something was very wrong.

Neighbours banded together and followed the tractor tracks. Finally, they found Ken. They called an ambulance, and he was rushed to the hospital.

Ken was in hospital for four weeks with a broken pelvis and broken ribs. In spite of the doctors' verdict that it would take a long, long time to recuperate, he was out walking around within a week of leaving the hospital and has now made an almost complete recovery.

And Nellie? In 1994, she was awarded the Ralston Purina Animal Hall of Fame Award for her bravery.

As far as Ken and Pauline know, Nellie had never heard the "go home" command before in her life. Yet she understood what Ken needed her to do. "She was sitting there watching me when I was trying to drag myself along," Ken says. "She knew there was something wrong with me." Ken was on the ground, badly hurt and suffering from shock and cold, for over two hours. If help hadn't come when it did, he might well have died.

"She got more cheese curds and baloney that day!" Pauline laughs.

TIA

The Labrador Who Retrieved a Boat

It was a cold, windy day. Heavy rain was falling. Sean Lingl and his friend Danny Parker were beginning to think their decision to go duck hunting was a mistake. Sitting between them, unmindful of the awful weather and eager to get to work, was Sean's chocolate Labrador Retriever, Tia.

They were paddling a small dinghy to an island in the mouth of the Nimpkish River, off northern Vancouver Island. The wind coming in against the current was whipping the water up into bigger and bigger waves. With the rain and the waves crashing over the bow, water was lapping around their feet and getting deeper by the minute.

The boat rocked alarmingly; paddling was getting more and more difficult. The dinghy was constructed with two layers of plastic hull. The air trapped between the layers was supposed to make the boat unsinkable. Unknown to Sean, however, there was a hole in the outermost layer, and the boat was taking on water. Suddenly, the dinghy heeled over to one side.

"We're in trouble," Sean yelled to Danny. "We'd better get back to shore."

They tried to turn the boat around, but the wind caught it. Instantly, it turned upside-down.

Sean found himself in the freezing water, clinging to the side of the overturned dinghy. Beside him, his friend Danny also clung to the boat. Tia was nowhere to be seen.

She must be trapped under the boat, Sean thought, and groped desperately for her. He found her and pulled her out. He let her go, thinking she would swim to shore.

After rescuing Tia, Sean turned his mind to his own problem. Both he and Danny were wearing chest-high hip waders. Sean was worried. He had heard stories of people being dragged down as their waders filled with water, and of trapped air in the high boots causing the wearer to flip upside-down.

And they were in the Pacific Ocean in the middle of winter. The water was frigid. If they didn't get out right away, the cold would kill them.

Suddenly, Sean realized that the boat was moving through the water. He looked ahead and saw Tia, the mooring line clenched firmly between her teeth, swimming strongly toward the shore. As soon as they realized what she was doing, Sean and Danny began to help as much as they could by kicking their feet.

They were about a hundred metres away from Vancouver Island, and the water was wild. But Tia ploughed steadily on. The two men's feet finally touched bottom and they staggered on shore.

Once on land, the wind cut through their soaked clothing. Now they were *really* cold. They ran the short distance to the truck, Tia romping at their heels. The *men* may have been suffering, but Labradors like nothing better than ice-cold water, and Tia was not at all the worse for her dip. Sean and Danny, however, were glad it was only a fifteen-minute drive home and to warm, dry clothes.

What Tia had done was so incredible that at first Sean was reluctant to tell anybody other than his wife, Marnie, about it. You see, Tia has only three legs.

Sean got Tia as a pup. Labrador Retrievers are dogs with immense amounts of energy, and they need a lot of exercise. Sean was in the habit of running her regularly. One day, there was a ditch filled with water beside the road they were on. If Labs see water, they *have* to be in it. It seems to be an unwritten rule. So of course Tia plunged joyfully into the ditch and ran through it. Unfortunately, someone must have thrown a bottle in there and it had broken. Tia yelped, and came out bleeding. Sean looked her over and found that she had cut the pad of her right back paw very badly.

Sean took her to his veterinarian, but because the cut was right through the pad, the vet was unable to stitch it. He bandaged it, and they tried to keep Tia off her feet. But in spite of their care, the foot became infected and the infection spread up into the leg. They sent Tia to an animal hospital in Campbell River. There, the doctors tried for three days to save her leg, but finally notified Sean that it would have to be amputated.

"We thought about getting her put to sleep," Sean says. "I didn't want to see her not able to move."

But the vet told him that chances were Tia would be able to get around fine with only three legs. "Actually, it often takes the owner longer to get used to it than the dog," he said.

Sean didn't want to lose Tia, so he agreed to the operation.

"She was grabbing sticks and wanting to run the first day we had her home," Sean says now. "We had to slow her down. She adapted right away. It was just like she never even knew it was gone."

Tia can run just about as fast as ever, and jump over anything in her path. The only time she has a bit of trouble is climbing hills or scrambling through rocky places. She went right back to her job of retrieving ducks for Sean when they went hunting, jumping out of the boat with no trouble at all. And fetching balls remains her favourite game. She never gets tired.

"When you're finished playing with her, she'll just want to keep on," Sean says. "She'll follow you around with that ball and then drop it on the ground in front of you and push with her nose until it rolls on your feet."

Like most Labs, Tia is also great with children. Sean's wife, Marnie, is from a big family, so in addition to their own two daughters, there are often eight or nine nieces and nephews around. Tia is often literally covered with children crawling all over her, pulling on her hair and her whiskers. She just lies there and loves it. She'll play rough with Sean, but when it comes to the children she's always gentle.

Tia was awarded the Ralston Purina Animal Hall of Fame Award for her intelligence and bravery, and thoroughly enjoyed the trip to Toronto with Sean and Marnie to receive it. VIP treatment at a big hotel, a special doggy sitter, and travelling by limousine everywhere she went suited her just fine.

And Sean Lingl and Danny Parker believe she deserved every bit of it.

Tia

The Yangtze Incident

A civil war raged throughout China between the years 1946 and 1949. After the end of the Second World War, two parties began their struggle for control of the country. The Nationalist Party was led by Chiang Kai-shek; the Communist Party was led by Mao Tsetung.

Britain was a neutral country — the British government wasn't supporting one party or the other — and maintained an embassy office at Nanking on the Yangtze River. In spite of Britain's neutrality, in April of 1949 the captain and crew of a British frigate, HMS *Amethyst*, found themselves right in the middle of the battle. . . .

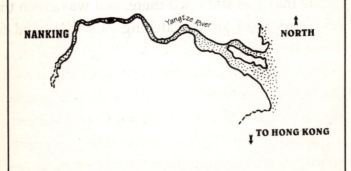

SIMON

The Ship's Cat

Simon, a black and white tomcat, was found as a kitten on Stonecutters' Island, off Hong Kong. He was brought on board the *Amethyst*, a British navy frigate that was stationed there, and was given the very important job of catching rats that tried to sneak aboard.

The cat soon became the crew's pet and mascot. He was a favourite especially with the younger seamen, and of Boy Seaman First Class Sid Horton in particular. At seventeen, Sid was the youngest on board. He had been in the navy since he was just a little over fifteen years old, and had never been in battle. That changed on April 20, 1949, one week after Sid joined the *Amethyst* crew.

Early that morning, the *Amethyst* was making its way up the Yangtze River in China, carrying supplies for the British Embassy at Nanking. The mist swirled over the ship's wake as it churned through the murky waters. On the north shore of the river was the Communist People's Liberation Army, with guns and heavy artillery (cannon) aimed across the river at the Nationalist Army of Chiang Kai-shek, positioned on the south bank.

Because Britain was not supporting one army or the other, the *Amethyst*'s captain, Lieutenant-Commander B.M. Skinner, expected safe passage. Still, he knew he should make his way through the fighting zone with caution. The Chinese Communists had already shot at the Nationalists on the south bank, and the *Amethyst* had to pass right between them.

At first the heavy fog cloaked the ship, but as the sun rose, the heat burned it off. The crew was tense and alert. At twenty minutes past nine, flame suddenly erupted from the north shore and a shell whined overhead. Seconds later it exploded, ripping apart the wheelhouse. The man at the wheel was hit and fell to one side, dragging the wheel to the left with him. The ship turned toward shore.

The *Amethyst* began to fight back, and the battle raged on for hours. Finally, after noon, the Communist guns fell silent. The crew of the *Amethyst* could take stock. Of 183 crew members, twenty-three were dead or dying and thirty-one were wounded, including the captain and his senior officers. The ship was so damaged that it was unsteerable. (It was found later that the ship had been hit fifty-three times.) It plowed into the mud of Rose Island, off the south bank, and stuck fast. As the lull in the fighting continued, the officers tried to move the ship out of the mud. They were successful, and managed to move the ship about a kilometre upriver. But every time they tried to make a break for safety, the Communists fired at them.

In all the confusion, no one had had time to think of Simon. But when things calmed down, Simon appeared. He was bleeding from a shrapnel wound, his fur was singed, his face burned. No one knew for certain what had happened to him, but his favourite sleeping place was on the captain's bed, and a shell had exploded in that cabin, knocking a hole in the hull right beside it.

The little cat hadn't lost his spirit, though. Rubbing affectionately against the legs of his friends as they assembled for a makeshift meal, he avidly wolfed down all the scraps they gave him. Sid Horton was especially glad to see that Simon had survived. (He himself had suffered a broken arm.) As he lay in his hammock that night, Sid heard scrabbling along the steam pipes that ran over his head. A rat scurried by, closely pursued by a sure-footed cat. Wounded or not, Simon was back on the job.

And Simon stayed on the job — for the next 101 days, as the *Amethyst* lay trapped in the Yangtze River. The men were able to trade with the villagers on shore for eggs, cabbages and other fresh vegetables, but even these were scanty. In spite of strict rationing, food began to run dangerously low. In the meantime, the daytime heat was sweltering and the rats multiplied at an alarming rate. But Simon kept pace with them. Although still suffering the after-effects of his wounds and burns, for three months he caught at least a rat a day — even though some of the rats were bigger than he was.

The *Amethyst* finally escaped on the last day of July. The captain planned the break-out carefully.

In the dark of night he slipped anchor and the *Amethyst* quietly began its run. It was a wild, almost blind sprint. The Yangtze was a river full of twists, turns and shoals, and no one aboard knew its waters. All the captain and crew had to navigate by was a set of charts which might be out of date. But bravely, making smoke for cover and weaving desperately to avoid the shells being fired at them, they dashed for freedom.

It was more than 200 kilometres to the mouth of the Yangtze. They made it just as the first rays of dawn were lightening the sky. News of their heroic exploit travelled fast, and the story of Simon, the Ship's Cat, travelled with it. When the men returned to Hong Kong, newspaper reporters and photographers were there to greet them. Sid Horton was given the honour of holding the cat for all the pictures the media wanted.

Simon was declared a hero. Back in England, he was awarded the Dickin Medal — the highest honour for animals — in recognition of his bravery under fire and for "disposing of many rats though wounded by a shell blast." He is buried now in Ilford, Essex, and the inscription on his tombstone reads:

"In Memory of Simon. Served in HMS *Amethyst* May 1948–November 1949. Throughout the Yangtze Incident his behaviour was of the highest order."

Simon

The "Newf"

Descended from Mastiffs brought by Basque fishermen to Canada, Newfoundlands are massive dogs with thick, double-layered, long black coats that protect them from the cold. They have very strong bones, and webbed paws that make them very much at home in the water. They used to work for fishermen, and would swim out to gather in the nets that their owners spread in the frigid waters off the Newfoundland coast.

Quite often the old sailing ships would have a Newfoundland dog on board to rescue unfortunate sailors who were washed overboard during storms. There are many stories of Newfoundland dogs who have performed heroic rescues. A Newfoundland once swam ashore with a line from a ship that was sinking off the coast of Nova Scotia and helped to haul the passengers and crew to safety. That Newf was awarded a medal from Lloyd's of London, the famous insurance company. Another Newfoundland, so the story goes, once saved the French emperor Napoleon from drowning. Newfoundlands are even used as lifeguards on some beaches in France.

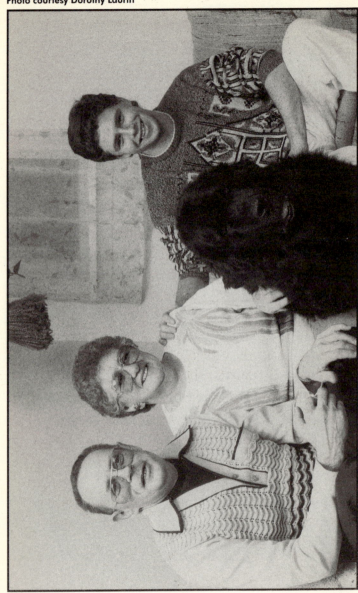

Shana with Dorothy, Herman and Kevin

SHANA

The Dog Who Conquered Her Own Greatest Fear to Save Her Owner

Shana was an intelligent, loving, even-tempered dog, typical of the Newfoundland in every way but one: she was afraid of the water.

Dorothy Laurin got Shana from a breeder in Pincher Creek, Alberta, when the pup was about seven weeks old. When Shana was nine months old, she made the mistake of leaning too far over the edge of a dock and fell in. It was her first experience with water. The pup panicked as the water closed over her head and she nearly drowned. By the time she figured out how to swim and got back to shore, she had decided that, Newfoundland or not, deep water was not for her.

Shana came from seven generations of champion show dogs, but Dorothy did not want to put her into the show ring. Instead, Shana became a beloved family pet. She absolutely adored children. On her walks through the city she would pass by every adult or dog she met without slowing down, but the minute she saw a child she'd get excited and want to play. She liked nothing better than to be harnessed up to Dorothy's son Kevin's wagon to give children rides. She would even help him deliver his newspapers on his newspaper route. Dorothy recalls the time Kevin had over 200 papers to deliver and asked his sister, Michele, to help him.

"I don't know your route," Michele protested.

"Shana does," Kevin answered.

So while he did one side of the road, Michele did the other with Shana. The big, black-haired dog pulled the wagon and stopped at every house that took the paper. She knew the route, all right!

Shana was never one for playing with a ball, but she did love fluffy slippers. Every Christmas she received a new pair as a present. No — she didn't wear them! She would sit on the floor, slipper in her mouth, and Kevin would grasp the other end for a lively game of tug-of-war. With all the strength Shana had in her powerful muscles, she'd pull him right across the floor. She was also best friends with the family cat; they could often be found curled up sleeping together.

Grooming Shana was sometimes a bit of a challenge. Although she liked it once the brushing actually started, she would worry at the first sight of the brush and comb. Dorothy remembers one time when her husband, Herman, got out the grooming equipment and Shana took a flying leap onto the couch, trying — unsuccessfully — to hide her fifty-five kilogram bulk behind poor Kevin.

Shana loved it out in the bush, and had her own tent for camping with the family. She never got as far as swimming at a beach, but she did have her own private pool. Dorothy and Herman bought her a children's wading pool to cool off in during the summer heat. It was shallow, and only just big enough for her to lie down in, so she didn't find it threatening. In fact, on hot summer nights Shana would often want to go out, and as Dorothy and Herman waited impatiently to let her back in, they would hear water splashing. Shana was having a midnight dip.

Then came the freak storm that hit Calgary, Alberta, on August 16, 1988. Dorothy and Herman were sitting outside their house that evening, talking to their neighbour and watching him cut his lawn. It was peaceful and warm — they had no hint at all of what was about to occur. The neighbour happened to look up at the sky at seven o'clock.

"I'd better hurry up," he said. "Looks like it's going to rain." The clouds were black and coming up fast. Dorothy and Herman went inside.

A heavy rain began, and within minutes it was pelting down. Then came the hail. The water rose as first streets, then lawns became flooded. There was a crash from below and the sound of breaking glass. Dorothy and Herman rushed downstairs to find that a basement window had caved in with the pressure and the house was starting to fill with water. Dorothy headed for the front door, closely followed by her husband, but the moment she opened it, she found herself engulfed and carried away in a torrent of rushing water. The street had been transformed into a raging, ice-filled river.

"There was nothing to hold on to," Dorothy says.

"I was really struggling. If I had gone under I would not have been able to get out."

She screamed for help, but before her husband could do anything, Shana, the dog who was deathly afraid of deep water, dove in. Without the slightest hesitation she swam toward her floundering owner. Dorothy managed to grab hold of her long, thick fur and hold on. Swimming powerfully, Shana towed her to safety at the neighbours' house on higher ground.

It was only half an hour from the time Dorothy and Herman had been sitting, talking with their neighbour, until the time of Dorothy's rescue. But in that short time, they lost everything in their basement. Kevin's and Michele's bedrooms were down there, as well as a laundry room, sewing room and bathroom. The water rose right to the ceiling, and everything in those rooms was either swept away or destroyed — nothing could be salvaged.

Michele was away on holiday — the few clothes she had with her were all she had left of her belongings. Kevin lost everything he owned, as well. Luckily he was working that evening. It was his window that gave way, and if he had been in his room with his door closed, he would have been in trouble when the water cascaded in.

Shana received two awards for her heroism and was the subject of many news stories, including an article in *Dogs in Canada* magazine. Sadly, Shana died of cancer when she was nine years old, in October 1992. She will never be forgotten by Dorothy Laurin, however, nor by her family. Shana was a dog who could surmount her own worst fear in order to save her best friend.

CHARLIE

The Dog Who Believed In Returning a Favour

Charlie is a Husky–German Shepherd mix with a thick, soft coat the colour of creamed honey and big, dark brown eyes. He's the kind of dog you look twice at on the street. It wasn't always like this. His owner, Tom Van Impe, found him at an animal shelter in Hamilton when Charlie was about a year and a half old, and he was very different.

"He was the most pathetic, sad little pup you've ever seen," Tom says. "But beautiful, too. You could see he had the potential of becoming a lovely dog."

Tom was probably the only one who could see

that. Charlie had been abused, he was sick, his coat was in tatters and ragged and he was as thin as a rail. He was frightened of every sudden movement, of every loud noise. At that point he was a sorry, sickly excuse for a dog.

Their first few months together were difficult. In addition to being frightened of every sudden noise — a car backfiring, even the crackling of a fire — Charlie cringed when Tom so much as picked up a broom. He resisted being cared for and ran away at every opportunity. Tom had to retrieve the dog from the animal shelter four or five times. He began to think he had taken on an impossible task.

Gradually, however, Charlie settled down. Secure in Tom's friendship and care, the dog even began to relax and enjoy life. Tom was able to take him along when he went to work, cutting lawns in the area. Riding in Tom's truck became fun, and Charlie loved it when Tom's customers would come out to pet him.

Then, one night, Tom's house caught fire. It was very late autumn, almost early winter. The house was heated with a wood-burning stove; Tom hadn't gotten around to installing a smoke alarm yet. A friend was sleeping on the couch in the living room.

About three in the morning, Tom was awakened by Charlie. The dog had come into the room and was "barking like crazy."

"I thought he had to go out," Tom says, "and I'd already let him out at midnight, so I just said, 'No, it's too early. Come on, Charlie, we're not going out now, go back to sleep.' I rolled over and tried to get back to sleep myself. No way would he let me, though. He grabbed my arm and pulled me right out of bed. He was actually growling at me! When I hit the floor, I saw the smoke and realized something was wrong."

Somehow, a spark from the stove had started a fire. Tom rushed to alert his friend. The two men and Charlie managed to get out of the burning house and call the fire department, but by the time the fire was brought under control, the house had suffered a lot of damage. Firemen at the scene said that Tom and his friend could easily have died from the smoke alone. The dog that Tom had nursed back to health, fed, and made a friend of had repaid him by saving his life.

Tom is married now, and the household has expanded. Charlie accepted Carol and her three sons with immediate affection — but wasn't too sure about Kitty. He and Kitty have since become the best of friends, along with all the other animals. There's another cat, Ti-Cat, and another dog, Rocky. There are even a couple of turtles — big ones. Charlie did sort of gnaw on one once while Tom was cleaning out the tank, but he only chipped a little piece of the shell.

Charlie starts his days off by jostling the bed, rolling over on his back, and demanding a belly rub. A friendly, happy, contented family dog, he's a far cry from the miserable little pup Tom brought home with him all those years ago.

"I really believe that Charlie knew I had saved his life by giving him a good home," Tom says. "He returned the favour by saving mine. He's become my best friend. There's nowhere we don't go together if we can."

Charlie was awarded the Ralston Purina Animal Hall of Fame Award for his act of bravery.

And Tom bought a smoke alarm.

Photo courtesy Tom Van Impe

Charlie and Tom

From Playful Pup to Guide Dog

Guide dogs are carefully bred. When guide dog pups are six to eight weeks old, they are sent out to a foster home. There, for the next year or so, they live like normal dogs — or almost like normal dogs. Their temporary owners give the dogs love and affection, but they know that these pups are being prepared for one of the most important careers a dog can have — guide dog for the blind. While they are still young, the foster-owners train the dogs to deal with all kinds of situations. The pups are walked on busy streets, taken on buses, trains and subways, into restaurants and through crowded malls. They are exposed to loud noises, sudden disturbances and exciting distractions. And they are encouraged to play with and tolerate children.

When the dogs are about fourteen months old they return to the guide dog centre where they undergo five to nine months of more intense training. Not all young dogs make it. The ones who do are finally ready to be matched up.

Just as the dogs are carefully chosen, so are their potential owners. An applicant for a guide dog is screened very thoroughly. Once he or she has been approved, the guide dog trainers select the dog they think is the right one. The blind person is brought to the centre to go through an intensive training course with his or her new canine partner. By the end, dog and human have bonded in a very special relationship.

Dogs can also be trained to be the hearing ears of a deaf person and to stand guard over or fetch help for someone having an epileptic seizure. They can even do all sorts of small jobs for people in wheelchairs. Helper dogs mean freedom and independence for their owners — and they are the most faithful and loyal companions a human being could ever hope for.

FLOYD

The Gentle Giant

"I'd walk down the street and hear footsteps coming toward me. Then I'd hear them slowing down. Then I'd hear them go *way* around me — or even across the street."

Seeing Glen Murphy's guide dog, Floyd, coming toward you on a narrow sidewalk, you'd likely make room, too. Floyd is one of the biggest German Shepherds you're ever likely to meet. Sitting at his ease, this dog could rest his nose quite comfortably on your dining room table, and from nose to tail he's almost as long as a bicycle.

Glen got Floyd when he was a second year

student at the University of Calgary. Because Glen was in the middle of classes and couldn't take time off, the Canadian Guide Dogs for the Blind, located in Manotick, Ontario, flew Floyd and his trainer out to Glen. There they went through an intensive three week training course. They used Glen's own normal routes as their training ground, and soon Floyd knew the way to the bus stop, the bus route, and how to find, by name, every building that Glen went to on campus.

Floyd learned the routines quickly and well, so well that he even worked out shortcuts to some of the buildings on his own. And despite his size, he proved to be very gentle. Glen says, "He's the kind of dog you only have to speak softly to. If you ever raised your voice he'd get hurt really quickly. People thought he must be really hard to control, but he was so gentle on the hard handle [the special harness that guide dogs wear] and leash that with just a subtle command and a little flick of your fingers he worked beautifully.

"He is big, though," Glen adds. "He decided to stand up and put his paws on my shoulders one day. I'm tall enough — about 5 foot 10 inches [175 centimetres] — but he was taller than me!"

Floyd learned very quickly that Glen was his responsibility, and he was always protective. Glen studies karate, and it was hard to convince Floyd that Glen didn't need his protection when he was fighting. One evening it proved too much for Floyd. Glen's friend Mike came over to where Glen was sitting at a tournament one night, and gave him a friendly whack on the shoulder with a rolled-up brochure. Big mistake.

In an instant, Glen felt Floyd jump up, and he heard his friend cry, "Glen! Glen!"

"What's going on?" Glen asked.

"Your dog! Your dog!"

Glen reached down. Floyd had Mike pinned right to the ground. Mike was a big man, about a hundred kilograms, but Floyd wasn't letting him go anywhere. He wasn't biting Mike, but he had Mike's arm in his mouth, right by the wrist where the rolled-up paper was, and he wasn't letting him so much as move. Glen let the dog stand on his friend for a couple of minutes, then said, "Okay, Floyd." The dog let Mike go. "I never trained him to do that," Glen adds. "He just did it, instinctively."

Glen has good reason to be thankful for Floyd's

protective instinct, for it probably saved his life. Guide dogs are heroic dogs every day of their lives — every time a squirrel runs in front of their noses and they don't chase it. But Floyd went one step further.

Glen was boarding with his mother at the time. One night, she was awakened by Floyd grabbing and tugging at her arm. She got up and he pulled her down to Glen's bedroom. Glen was lying on the floor, unconscious and bleeding. She rushed to call 9-1-1; the paramedics and ambulance officers were there within minutes.

Glen was healthy and active, and had never shown any signs of epilepsy. But that night, with no warning, his body began to shake violently. As the seizure went on, he fell out of bed and hit his head.

When the paramedics started working on Glen, his mother tried to coax Floyd away, but the dog would have none of it. He broke away from her and returned to the bedside. Uneasy and more than a little scared, the paramedics let the dog stay only when they realized Glen was blind and this was his guide dog. And over the next few days, while Glen was recovering, Floyd rarely left his room.

Glen had a concussion, and was out of school for

a few weeks. The epilepsy was brought under control, but the seizure left him with a kind of amnesia. He was a month into the semester at university, but he had no memory at all of having attended classes. He went through the notes he had taped and then transcribed into Braille, and couldn't remember ever taking them.

Glen had to drop half his courses, and work on relearning everything he'd forgotten. He would not have had the courage to go back to school if it had not been for Floyd. "In fact, I couldn't have done it without Floyd," he says. "The walk to the bus, the long bus ride, and then getting around the campus — I would never have been able to do it if I had had to use a cane." During this difficult time, Floyd was not only Glen's eyes, but his memory. There was always the fear of having another seizure in the street, too, but Glen knew that he was safe with Floyd. The dog would never leave him.

"I really sometimes wonder what would have happened to me that night if Floyd hadn't got my mom up," Glen says. "People sometimes die during seizures. Floyd just sort of stuck with me and never left my side, ever. He's a great dog."

Floyd is retired now, and Glen has a new dog —

a Labrador Retriever named Rusty. Floyd has fitted in beautifully with his new family, Dave and Audrey MacDonald and their teenage daughters, Lindsay and Holly. They couldn't love him more or be more proud of him. He has learned to relax and enjoy life — it's not unusual to see him lying in the sun on the front lawn with children all over him. His guide dog days are over and he's enjoying a well-earned rest — but he still walks Audrey carefully around puddles.

Photo courtesy Glen Murphy

Floyd and Glen

Samantha and Donald

Samantha

The Motherly Dog

There was a dog at the stable where Alana Tintse rode. The dog was a German Shepherd, possibly mixed with a bit of Husky. The people who ran the stable had found her — she was either lost or abandoned. Although she was friendly, they didn't really want the timid, cowering dog around. Alana's coach was on the point of taking the dog to the Society for the Prevention of Cruelty to Animals (SPCA) shelter, but Alana was determined to find a home for her. Unable to take the dog herself, she asked some friends, Brian and Michelle Holmes, if they would take the dog in.

"Oh, sure," said Michelle. "We'll take another dog." They named her Samantha.

The Holmes already had a dog, Monty, a mixed-breed pup. At first Samantha seemed determined to lose him. She would lead Monty off on long explorations — and happily return home without him. Brian Holmes had many a call to go and fetch him back. But around the time Monty figured out how to find his own way home, Samantha's mothering instincts kicked in. She became very protective of him, and the two dogs are always together now.

When the Holmes family dogsits a friend's Yorkshire Terrier and Llasa Apso, Samantha is in her glory looking after the two small dogs. She found Whoopi, the Yorkshire Terrier, once when she was lost in the woods. "Mind you," says Brian, "I think at first Samantha thought Whoopi was a squirrel!" She is even gentle with Brian's chickens and ducks.

Samantha is especially fond of children. When Brian takes her along in his truck into town and she sees children playing at recess in a schoolyard, she goes wild wanting to get out and play with them. Any child who comes to visit is welcomed and well licked, and the four Holmes grandchildren are special favourites.

One day Brian was home alone working on his computer. Monty was in the house with him. Brian heard Monty barking and went to the door to see if anyone had driven up. What he saw was Samantha with a little child hanging on to her, his arms wrapped around her neck. When Samantha saw Brian, she stopped, turned around, and started to lick the child. Brian grabbed his coat.

It was February, the snow was deep, and the temperature was hovering around ten degrees Celsius below zero, with a wicked wind. The child was dressed only in a light jacket, unbuttoned, and with no hat. He had mittens, but they were hanging on strings beside his bare hands. He wasn't crying, but he was shaking with cold.

Brian looked around. There was nobody else there. He tried to find out the boy's name, but couldn't make out what he was saying. Again, he looked around, trying to see if there was an adult anywhere near. He even ran quickly down his own long driveway, thinking that, because it was so icy out, a car might have slid into the ditch.

The only car he found was a little yellow

battery-operated car, a child's ride-on toy, abandoned out on the snowy road. Brian picked it up and put it in his driveway where it could be seen from the road, then hurried to get the boy inside the house.

Once inside, he took the boy's jacket off and started rubbing his hands. The child accepted Brian's help trustingly, and soon began to warm up. The cookie Brian gave him helped too. Brian kept asking questions. He thought the boy said his name was Ronald, then gradually made out that the boy was going "to see Mommy and the new baby."

Brian called the Ontario Provincial Police. By the time they arrived, a very worried father had also turned up.

It seemed that three-year-old Donald — that was actually his name — had woken early that morning and had decided to take his battery-operated car to the hospital where his mother and new baby sister were. He dressed himself as well as he could — even managed to get his boots on — and set out while his dad was still asleep. The little car's batteries died about a kilometre away from home, right at Brian and Michelle Holmes's driveway.

No one knows for certain what happened then,

but Samantha, who was outside, found him. Donald must have grabbed onto her for warmth and comfort, and she pulled him home to Brian.

The OPP reported to Brian the next day that the child was suffering from hypothermia (a dangerous lowering of his body's inner temperature). The area around the Holmes's house is fairly isolated, and if Samantha hadn't found Donald, he might well have died. The police were pleased to have a story with such a happy ending to report, and they sent out a press release. Reporters and camera crews were quick to arrive, and Samantha became famous. She was on CBC Radio Noon, on television, and in all the area papers. That spring she was selected to receive the Ontario SPCA "Hero of the Year" award.

And Donald's mother has promised to keep the motherly dog supplied with dog biscuits for the rest of her life.

Euchre and Constable Killens

EUCHRE

Dog With a Duty

Senior Constable Don Killens of the Ontario Provincial Police got Euchre (pronounced Yu-ker) when the dog was a year and a half old. Euchre had belonged to an elderly couple who decided that the cute little pup they had brought home had just become too much for them.

The large, dark German Shepherd passed all initial tests and his training with flying colours. He was no longer a pet, but a career dog. And what a career! During his working life, Euchre assisted in tracking down and capturing criminals and found or helped to find many people lost in the area around Perth, Ontario, where Senior Constable Killens is based.

There are plenty of stories about Euchre. Criminals may not have been too pleased with Euchre's successful tracking abilities, but many others, such as Bill Beattie, have reason to be grateful. Bill was on a photography expedition to the east end of Algonquin Park when he fell down a cliff. He was trapped on the cliffside. Four days later, thirsty and tired, he had just about reached the end of his endurance. It was then that a large, dark-coloured dog bounded over to him, licked his face and lay down beside him. Euchre had picked up his scent — off the wind.

Euchre's work was often hazardous, tracking armed and dangerous people. But he had one important advantage.

"Dogs track silently, and we are often in so fast we surprise the bad guys," says Constable Killens. He adds with a smile, "Then I just say to them: 'You've been Euchred!'" (Euchre is a card game. "You've been euchred!" is the phrase a player uses when he or she slaps down a winning hand.)

Once Euchre found more than a bad guy. He and Constable Killens were tracking a criminal who had robbed a house, when suddenly Euchre veered from the trail and started nosing something. Constable Killens looked down and saw a week-old pup lying whimpering on the ground. He scooped it up and carried it along. Soon after, Euchre managed to track the thief down, and he was arrested. In his pocket was another week-old pup. The OPP officers were able to connect the pups to the robbery, and both were returned unharmed to their mother.

The gentle, patient side of Euchre's nature was put to work as well. Constable Killens often took him to schools for demonstrations, and he went along to Toronto's Hospital for Sick Children when all sixteen OPP dog handlers presented a donation to the hospital.

"He would talk," Constable Killens says. "I would tell him to say goodbye to a classroom of kids and he would bark. I took him into classes often and he thought that was great. I would show them the basic program, then have him go over jumps and climb things. Then I'd take the kids outside and pick a student and show how Euchre could track them. You have to give your dog a lot of praise," he added. "Euchre would roll over to have his belly scratched."

Euchre even helped to guard the Pope and the Queen of England during visits to Canada. In all, he was just about the perfect example of a good police dog. And he was more than that: on a cool, mid-April Saturday early in his career, Euchre became a hero.

Constable Killens and Euchre had not been working together for long when the call came in. A seventeen-year-old boy was missing in the bush near Crosby, Ontario. The boy, Christian, had his dog, Spud, with him. He was visiting from Montreal, and didn't know the area at all. No one knew where he had gone. As well, Christian had health problems and it was very important that he be found quickly. A massive search was organized.

Constable Killens and Euchre, as well as another officer and his dog, were called in around six o'clock that night to help with the search. It was about five degrees Celsius, and foggy, with a light drizzle falling.

"So foggy you couldn't see in front of you," Constable Killens says, "so I knew I was going to have trouble finding Christian."

The fog that made it hard to see, however, helped

Euchre. Fog means moisture, and the more moisture there is in the air, the easier it is to track. Tracker dogs are so highly skilled they can follow rafts in the water, and even flakes of human skin or tiny threads that fall off clothing. They can track right through towns and into the country, following scents that are days old. Even so, it was late evening by now, and the trail was getting cold. Euchre needed all the help he could get.

With Euchre on his three-metre tether, the officers and their dogs began searching for scent. They searched through the night and on into the next morning. If Euchre got off on a wrong scent, they would just return and try again.

"We work and use every advantage we can," Constable Killens says. "We go to spots where no one else has gone. I was working downwind of where we thought the boy was, so this was working to my advantage."

By three-thirty Sunday morning more searchers were called in, including a helicopter and a third dog. Many local volunteers were among those trying desperately to locate Christian during that long, cold night.

The search finally ended about ten o'clock that

morning, when Euchre picked Christian's scent off the wind.

"Once they lock onto that scent you just help them and encourage them as much as you can," Constable Killens says. He did just that, and suddenly looked up to find Christian, cold and shivering, standing in front of him.

"How are you?" he asked.

"F-fine," the boy managed to get out.

Christian and Spud were taken back to a very grateful family. In spite of the cold and exposure, Christian had survived with no lasting ill effects.

"We find about two people a year who would have died otherwise, on average," Constable Killens says. "Finding a lost person is everything you work for. I've got the best job in the OPP."

Constable Killens works with another dog now, since Euchre died. Euchre worked faithfully for Constable Killens and the Ontario Provincial Police for almost six years — a long time in the life of a career dog.

Police Tracking Dogs

Most dogs chosen to be police dogs are not bred especially for this kind of work. Some may be rejects from breeders who know they won't do well in the show ring. Some are dogs who have been training to guide the blind and have proven to be too aggressive for this duty. Some come from owners who couldn't handle them. Many are found through newspaper ads.

Police dog handlers want a dog that is excited and eager to retrieve objects, that is physically and mentally strong, and that isn't gun shy. They look for a dog that isn't scared of people. In a staring match, they want the dog to stare the officer down! Several breeds are good at sniffing out bombs or drugs, but German Shepherds do most of the tracking. They are strong, able to work in hot or cold temperatures, and seem to have the best temperament for the job: aggressive, but not overly ferocious.

After undergoing a thorough health examination, each dog is carefully matched up with a police officer, to make a K-9 team. Together, dog and handler go through an intense fourteen-week course, starting with basic obedience training. The dog is trained to climb ladders and stairs and scale walls as high as seven feet. It must be able to jump through windows, climb barrels, balance and walk on a thin beam and jump more than ten feet forward from a standing position. Then the dog is trained in tracking and sniffing.

The dogs are also trained to protect their handlers. If the police officer is struck by a suspect, the K-9 partner will attack without hesitation. Many officers owe their lives to their dogs.

The dog lives with his handler in an outside kennel at the handler's home. The K-9 officer drives a special vehicle to transport his or her dog, and the team must be prepared to respond to a call anytime, day or night. But, although the bond that forms between officer and dog is a strong one, it is a working relationship — the dog is not a pet. And every six weeks, the K-9 team returns for refresher courses to keep up their skills.

The Rabbit Who Joined
the Navy

When the Second World War broke out, Jock McGregor was living in the United States. He was a British subject and wanted to fight for his country, but he couldn't get back to England. He came to Canada instead, and joined the Royal Canadian Navy.

"It was a very very fortunate thing for me," he says. "I made many good friends and I'll always treasure this decision."

After a few years he was drafted to the *Haida*, a

Canadian destroyer that, in 1944, was making nightly trips into the English channel to search for German submarines and do battle. During Jock's tour of duty the ship had many mascots, but there is one he remembers most fondly.

One night after some of the ship's crew had been on shore leave in Plymouth, they came back aboard with a baby rabbit. They put it on Jock's gun platform. In the morning, when he went to clean his guns and get them ready for action, there was the little rabbit, about eight centimetres long, sitting up and begging like a dog.

Jock went ashore and asked for help from the Wrens, the women's branch of the Royal Navy. They managed to find some dandelion leaves, and together they and Jock filled a whole bag full — enough to last a rabbit at sea for a long time.

The rabbit grew and grew and grew. The ship's doctor warned Jock that rabbits have very sensitive hearing. If the ship went into action, the shock of the gun noise would probably kill it. He advised Jock to get rid of the rabbit, but Jock couldn't bear to part with it.

The ship did see action. The rabbit not only survived, but became a pet of the whole ship. Then one night one of the stokers came up carrying a bin full of potatoes. The rabbit, which was tame by this time, heard the footsteps and hopped over, probably hoping it was Jock coming with more dandelion greens. The stoker didn't see the small animal and slammed the potato locker down on its leg. The leg was broken.

Jock took the rabbit to the ship's doctor. At first the doctor thought it should just be put out of its misery, but Jock persuaded him to splint the leg. The doctor did so, with two tiny pieces of wood and some plaster of paris.

"It hopped about like a little wounded sailor," Jock says.

About the fourth day the rabbit started to chew on the plaster until it fell off. Jock found that the leg had healed well and the rabbit was fine, although still limping.

The ship's doctor had been right about one thing, however. The rabbit *did* have very sensitive hearing — and a unusual talent. Normally quiet and peaceful, from time to time the rabbit would suddenly begin to squeak and hop about. Though puzzled at first by the rabbit's agitation, the crew of the *Haida* soon learned what it meant: the enemy was approaching. Forewarned, they prepared for battle. The crew grew quite confident about the rabbit's mysterious forecasting abilities.

After some time at sea the *Haida* sank a German submarine. Jock was the one who saw it surfacing and opened fire. The news of the victory was reported in the newspapers back in England, along with the story of the rabbit. The Duchess of Kent wrote a letter to Jock, asking if his rabbit could join the mascot club of the United Kingdom because it had survived all the action the *Haida* had seen. Jock filled out the application she sent, as did Captain Harry de Wolfe. The rabbit signed with its paw, pressed in a pad of ink and stamped on the application.

The Duchess of Kent sent Jock a grateful letter and a medal for the rabbit. The medal was for fidelity, which means faithfulness. Jock believes this is the only rabbit in the world to hold such an honour.

After the war, the rabbit lived peacefully in Halifax with Captain de Wolfe. The *Haida* is now permanently moored at the Toronto waterfront, and is open to visitors who would like to see the ship — the home, for a while, of a brave little rabbit.